About Us

Jack M. Offman, "Best Selling" Author

Jack M. Offman, the undiscovered gem of questionable children's novels, is a 40-something who finds joy in the nerdy realm of laser tag and video games—probably why he's still single. While his books might often get the silent treatment, he passionately dives into them after introspective beach walks and avoiding DUIs. And for the record, he's the kind of guy who'd never risk a sprint with scissors. Legends say his zest for life might just be infectious, if anyone bothered to listen.

Anita V. Gina, God's Gift to Illustration

Anita V. Gina, a vivacious 20-something illustrating sensation, is certain she's the glitzy sequin in the artsy universe. Fully convinced that her fingers drip 24-karat magic, she's taken on the brave challenge of converting Jack M. Offman's poetic trainwrecks into bestsellers because, let's face it, she thinks he's about as artistic as a soggy... you get it. Though schooled in the classics, she's confident that her art game is so tight, Picasso might've begged her for a masterclass. Her dating profiles? The stuff of legends! But bafflingly, she's still single, always swiping left, wondering, "Why can't these dudes level up to my grandmaster canvas?"

Cleveland Steamer Press, Trash Book Publisher

Ah, Cleveland Steamer Press – surprisingly not from Cleveland and inspired by something so unsavory, we dare not speak its name. This publishing marvel somehow attracts authors even a garbage disposal might reject. Continually defying economic logic (never having turned a profit), this powerhouse pumps out "children's books" so dubious they're on society's blacklist. Truly, their books are best reserved for foes – consider them a paperweight with a vendetta.

THE BLOW JOB
FELT AROUND THE WORLD

Stan's Breezy Tale of Purpose and Play

Jack M. Offman & Anita V. Gina

ClevelandSteamerPress.com

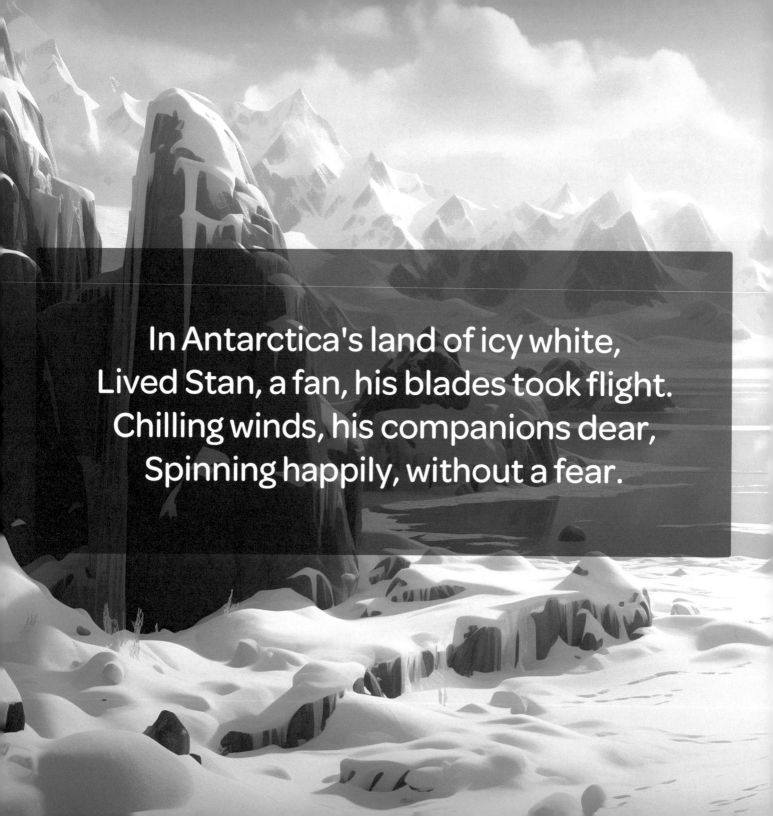

In Antarctica's land of icy white,
Lived Stan, a fan, his blades took flight.
Chilling winds, his companions dear,
Spinning happily, without a fear.

With each gust, he'd dream and sway,
Of broader horizons, far away.
Penguin pals like Jake and Steve,
Played catch with joy, never to leave.

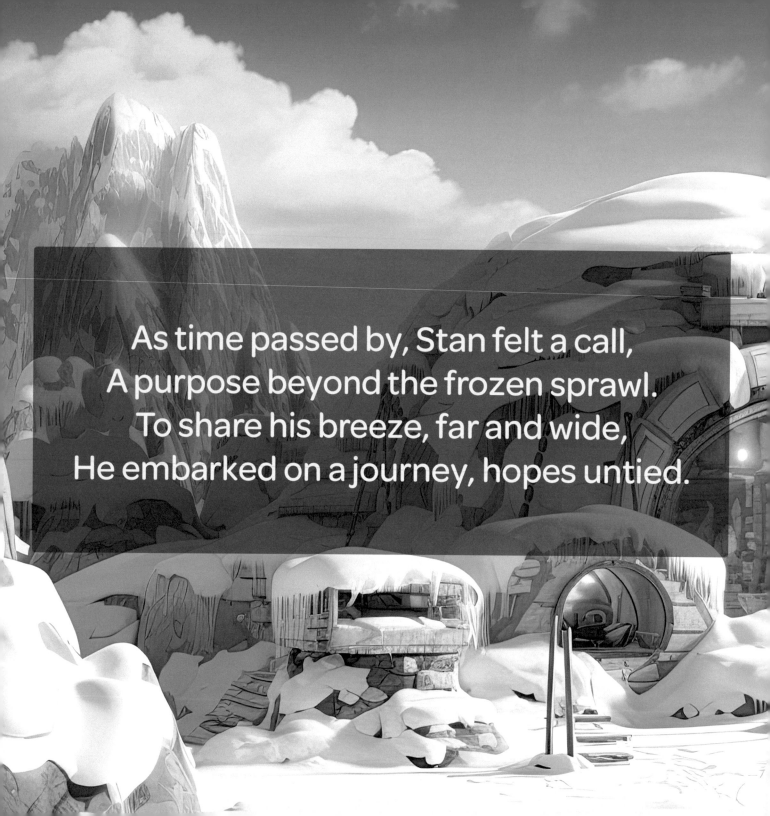

As time passed by, Stan felt a call,
A purpose beyond the frozen sprawl.
To share his breeze, far and wide,
He embarked on a journey, hopes untied.

First, to the south, his wind did roar,
But penguins had winds aplenty, and more.
Northward he went, seeking a place,
To find a welcome, a new embrace.

But in the north, a similar view,
Penguins content with their wind, true.
Stan pondered, seeking his role anew,
His gusty heart searching for a clue.

A ship he boarded, destiny unknown,
Sailing far, seeking a place to be shown.
To Brazil's shores, he came, so hot,
A land of warmth, a different plot.

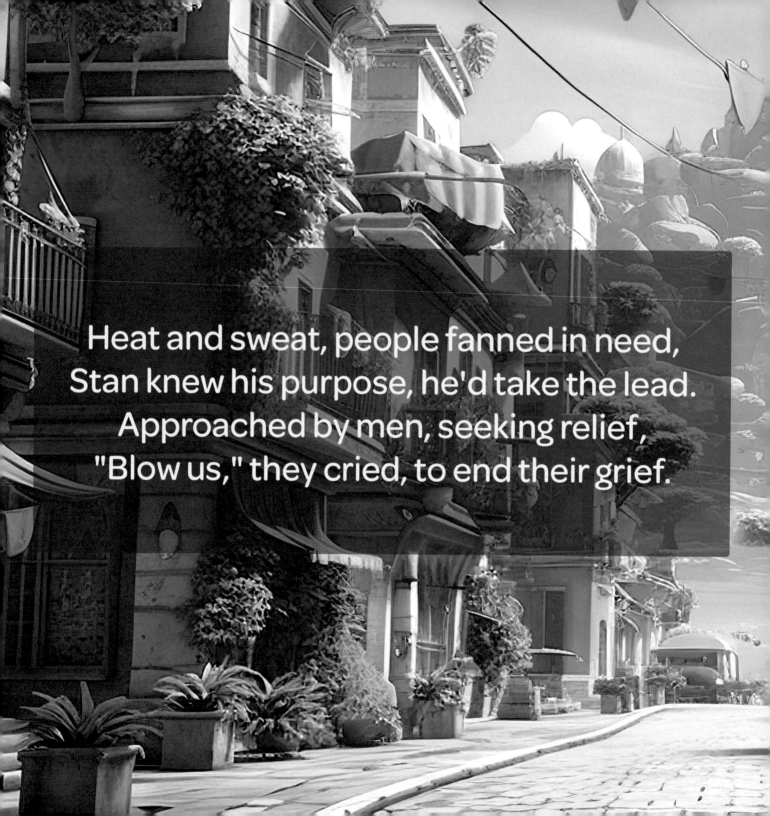

Heat and sweat, people fanned in need,
Stan knew his purpose, he'd take the lead.
Approached by men, seeking relief,
"Blow us," they cried, to end their grief.

Blades spun fast, wind's force untamed,
Men flew back, their cheeks inflamed.
A crowd gathered, amazed by his might,
A spectacle wondrous, a thrilling sight.

Stan found his place, in Brazil's embrace,
Blowing men & women, at a blistering pace.
A lesson he learned, purpose can roam,
He found his job, blowing far from home.

Blowing people, his task with zest,
Bringing comfort, his blow was blessed.
Stan, the fan, found his unique role,
Bringing joy to all, he achieved his goal.

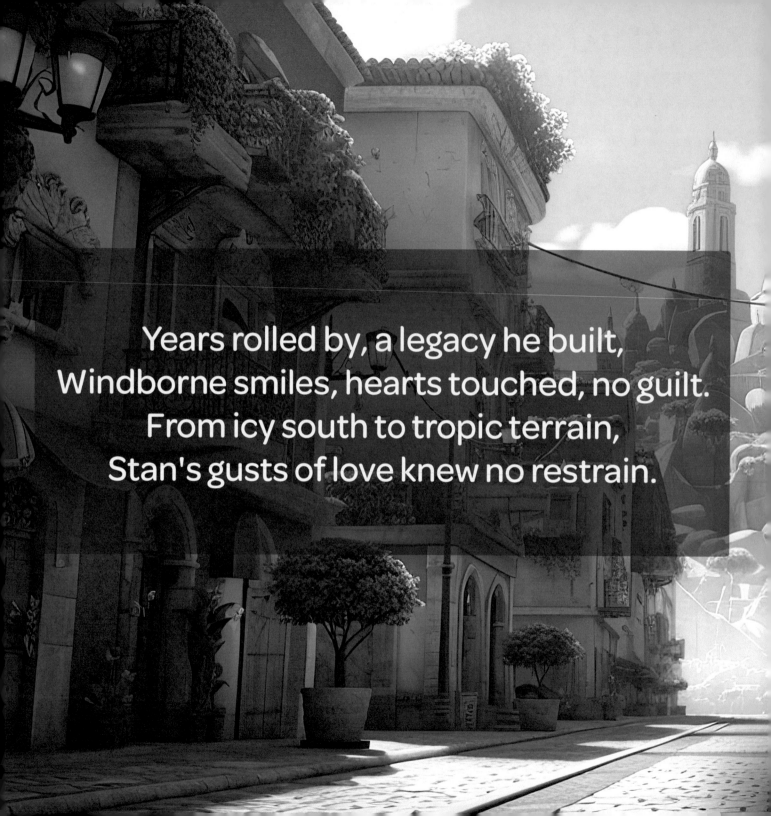

Years rolled by, a legacy he built,
Windborne smiles, hearts touched, no guilt.
From icy south to tropic terrain,
Stan's gusts of love knew no restrain.

Now his tale's told, across the land,
Of a fan named Stan, who blew so grand.
Dreams take flight, beyond the ice,
A job well done, so kind and nice.

...and remember

...nothing brings the world together like a good blow job!

The End

...Stay tuned for more stories
that will blow your mind!

Hey Legend!

Book-writing is a grind, and we truly appreciate you not only buying this book, but hacking your way all the way through. Hopefully, you didn't upend any kid's birthday parties or religious gatherings!

The fun shouldn't stop here, and guess what? YOU hold the ticket to keep this steam-boat chugging.

Some quick ways to keep our dreams alive:

Rate This Beast
Drop a hilariously honest review on Amazon or your purchase point. Got writer's block? Boot up ChatGPT or Bard, and let the madness ensue. We'll be spotlighting the zaniest reviews on our socials. Let's make those critiques funnier than the book itself!

Prank & Delight Your Friends(or Enemies)
Noticed the QR Code? That's your gateway to more of our shenanigans. Ideal for those spontaneous giggle-bomb moments with friends or to send a clear message to someone you despise.

Feed Our Ramen Cravings
We've poured hours into this! Perhaps help us replenish our pantry with another instant noodle by snagging more of our reads. Same QR code works!

Steamily Yours,

The Cleaveland Steamer Press Crew

SCAN ME!

More hilarity by Cleveland Steamer Press

Our Friends & Parnters

Made in United States
Cleveland, OH
02 January 2025

12999922R10021